G000094788

THE ROYAL HORTICULTURAL SOCIETY

DIARY 2003

Commentary by Brent Elliott
Illustrations from the Royal Horticultural Society's Lindley Library

FRANCES LINCOLN

Frances Lincoln Limited
4 Torriano Mews
Torriano Avenue
London NW5 2RZ
www.franceslincoln.com

Website: www.rhs.org.uk

British Library cataloguing-in-publication data
A catalogue record for this book is available from the British Library

ISBN 0-7112-1911-7

Printed in China

First Frances Lincoln edition 2002

RHS FLOWER SHOWS 2003

All shows feature a wide range of floral exhibits staged by the nursery trade, with associated competitions reflecting seasonal changes and horticultural sundries. With the exception of the shows held at Malvern, Chelsea, Hampton Court, Tatton Park and Wisley, all RHS Flower Shows will be held in one or both of the Society's Horticultural Halls in Greycoat Street and Vincent Square, Westminster, London SW1

The dates given are correct at the time of going to press, but before travelling to a Show, we strongly advise you to check with the Diary Dates section of the RHS Journal *The Garden*, or telephone the 24-hour Flower Show Information Line (020 7649 1885) for the latest details.

FRONT COVER
Four cultivars (now vanished) of the corn poppy (*Papaver rhoeas*), engraved by Bartholomaeus Seuter, from the fourth volume of *Phytanthoza* (1745)

BACK COVER
Anemone cultivars, including two plush anemones, engraved by Bartholomaeus Seuter or Johann Jakob Haid, from the first volume of *Phytanthoza* (1737)

TITLE PAGE
Morina persica, engraved by Bartholomaeus Seuter, from the second volume of *Phytanthoza* (1739)

OVERLEAF, RIGHT
A variety of cherry, engraved by Johann Jakob Haid, from the second volume of *Phytanthoza* (1739)

CALENDAR 2003

January

M	T	W	T	F	S	S
		1	2	3	4	5
6	7	8	9	10	11	12
13	14	15	16	17	18	19
20	21	22	23	24	25	26
27	28	29	30	31		

February

M	T	W	T	F	S	S
					1	2
3	4	5	6	7	8	9
10	11	12	13	14	15	16
17	18	19	20	21	22	23
24	25	26	27	28		

March

M	T	W	T	F	S	S
					1	2
3	4	5	6	7	8	9
10	11	12	13	14	15	16
17	18	19	20	21	22	23
24	25	26	27	28	29	30
31						

April

M	T	W	T	F	S	S
	1	2	3	4	5	6
7	8	9	10	11	12	13
14	15	16	17	18	19	20
21	22	23	24	25	26	27
28	29	30				

May

M	T	W	T	F	S	S
			1	2	3	4
5	6	7	8	9	10	11
12	13	14	15	16	17	18
19	20	21	22	23	24	25
26	27	28	29	30	31	

June

M	T	W	T	F	S	S
						1
2	3	4	5	6	7	8
9	10	11	12	13	14	15
16	17	18	19	20	21	22
23	24	25	26	27	28	29
30						

July

M	T	W	T	F	S	S
	1	2	3	4	5	6
7	8	9	10	11	12	13
14	15	16	17	18	19	20
21	22	23	24	25	26	27
28	29	30	31			

August

M	T	W	T	F	S	S
				1	2	3
4	5	6	7	8	9	10
11	12	13	14	15	16	17
18	19	20	21	22	23	24
25	26	27	28	29	30	31

September

M	T	W	T	F	S	S
1	2	3	4	5	6	7
8	9	10	11	12	13	14
15	16	17	18	19	20	21
22	23	24	25	26	27	28
29	30					

October

M	T	W	T	F	S	S
		1	2	3	4	5
6	7	8	9	10	11	12
13	14	15	16	17	18	19
20	21	22	23	24	25	26
27	28	29	30	31		

November

M	T	W	T	F	S	S
					1	2
3	4	5	6	7	8	9
10	11	12	13	14	15	16
17	18	19	20	21	22	23
24	25	26	27	28	29	30

December

M	T	W	T	F	S	S
1	2	3	4	5	6	7
8	9	10	11	12	13	14
15	16	17	18	19	20	21
22	23	24	25	26	27	28
29	30	31				

CALENDAR 2004

January

M	T	W	T	F	S	S
			1	2	3	4
5	6	7	8	9	10	11
12	13	14	15	16	17	18
19	20	21	22	23	24	25
26	27	28	29	30	31	

February

M	T	W	T	F	S	S
						1
2	3	4	5	6	7	8
9	10	11	12	13	14	15
16	17	18	19	20	21	22
23	24	25	26	27	28	29

March

M	T	W	T	F	S	S
1	2	3	4	5	6	7
8	9	10	11	12	13	14
15	16	17	18	19	20	21
22	23	24	25	26	27	28
29	30	31				

April

M	T	W	T	F	S	S
			1	2	3	4
5	6	7	8	9	10	11
12	13	14	15	16	17	18
19	20	21	22	23	24	25
26	27	28	29	30		

May

M	T	W	T	F	S	S
					1	2
3	4	5	6	7	8	9
10	11	12	13	14	15	16
17	18	19	20	21	22	23
24	25	26	27	28	29	30
31						

June

M	T	W	T	F	S	S
	1	2	3	4	5	6
7	8	9	10	11	12	13
14	15	16	17	18	19	20
21	22	23	24	25	26	27
28	29	30				

July

M	T	W	T	F	S	S
			1	2	3	4
5	6	7	8	9	10	11
12	13	14	15	16	17	18
19	20	21	22	23	24	25
26	27	28	29	30	31	

August

M	T	W	T	F	S	S
						1
2	3	4	5	6	7	8
9	10	11	12	13	14	15
16	17	18	19	20	21	22
23	24	25	26	27	28	29
30	31					

September

M	T	W	T	F	S	S
		1	2	3	4	5
6	7	8	9	10	11	12
13	14	15	16	17	18	19
20	21	22	23	24	25	26
27	28	29	30			

October

M	T	W	T	F	S	S
				1	2	3
4	5	6	7	8	9	10
11	12	13	14	15	16	17
18	19	20	21	22	23	24
25	26	27	28	29	30	31

November

M	T	W	T	F	S	S
1	2	3	4	5	6	7
8	9	10	11	12	13	14
15	16	17	18	19	20	21
22	23	24	25	26	27	28
29	30					

December

M	T	W	T	F	S	S
		1	2	3	4	5
6	7	8	9	10	11	12
13	14	15	16	17	18	19
20	21	22	23	24	25	26
27	28	29	30	31		

INTRODUCTION

Weinmann's *Phytanthoza Iconographia* was the first botanical work published on the continent of Europe to be printed in colour. Colour printing had been pioneered in England in the 1720s, with a couple of works printed by Elisha Kirkall using mezzotint engraving. The mezzotint engraving process, which produced subtle shading from black to white, without the lines common to etchings or line engravings, had been developed in the latter half of the seventeenth century. Instead of black ink, Kirkall applied coloured inks to the copper plates before they were pressed on to the paper. The results were crude by modern standards, and the limits of skill, time and money meant that usually only one or two colours were used. But it was a beginning, and in the 1730s Weinmann took the process further.

Johann Wilhelm Weinmann (1683–1741) was a wealthy apothecary in Regensburg, Germany, who built up a fine collection of botanical art. In the 1730s Weinmann put his collection to use by financing a major publication based on it. He commissioned the botanist Johann Georg Nicolaus Dieterichs to write the text; after Dieterichs's death, this was continued by his son Ludwig Michael Dieterichs. Albrecht von Haller, the great naturalist, wrote a preface which recounted the history of botany up to the eighteenth century. When Weinmann himself died, Ambrosius Karl Bieler took over the editorship.

Publication began in 1734, although the four volumes bear dates from 1737 to 1745 on their title pages. A Dutch edition was begun even before the first volume was completed. In 1787 the plates were reissued, minus the text, and with Linnaean names added to the plates. Since the Royal Horticultural Society's copy of the *Phytanthoza* has the original 1734–45 letterpress but also has Linnaean names added to the plates, it appears likely that the process of updating the nomenclature began while the work was still in progress. The 1787 publication was therefore a means of standardizing what had become an uneven edition.

The work is alphabetically arranged, and because it was based on a collection of drawings, it is diverse in its styles of illustration. The plates were engraved by Bartholomaeus Seuter and Johann Elias Ridinger, with additions by Johann Jakob Haid; none of the original artists is named. The most famous of the artists whose work Weinmann collected was Georg Dionysius Ehret (1708–1770), widely regarded as the best botanical artist of his day. Ehret worked for Weinmann at the beginning of his career in the 1720s (and later sued him, alleging inadequate payment). Some of the plates may be based on Ehret's drawings, but no one has ever conclusively identified which are his.

Despite some crudities of colouring, the *Phytanthoza* remains the greatest achievement in botanical colour printing before the second half of the nineteenth century. Its use of colour printing means that it was the first published work whose plates systematically differentiated cultivated varieties by their colour patterns.

Brent Elliott
The Royal Horticultural Society

DECEMBER ~ JANUARY

30 Monday

31 Tuesday

1 Wednesday

New Year's Day
Holiday UK, Republic of Ireland, Canada, USA, Australia and New Zealand

2 Thursday

New Moon

Holiday, Scotland and New Zealand

3 Friday

4 Saturday

5 Sunday

WEEK 1

A citrus fruit, engraved by Johann Jakob Haid, from the third volume of *Phytanthoza* (1742)

JANUARY

Monday 6

Epiphany

Tuesday 7

Wednesday 8

Thursday 9

First Quarter

Friday 10

Saturday 11

Sunday 12

WEEK 2

Anemone cultivars, including two plush anemones, engraved by Bartholomaeus Seuter or Johann Jakob Haid, from the first volume of *Phytanthoza* (1737)

JANUARY

13 Monday

14 Tuesday

15 Wednesday

16 Thursday

17 Friday

18 Saturday *Full Moon*

19 Sunday

WEEK 3

A form of kale (*Brassica oleracea*), engraved by Bartholomaeus Seuter or Johann Jakob Haid, from the first volume of *Phytanthoza* (1737)

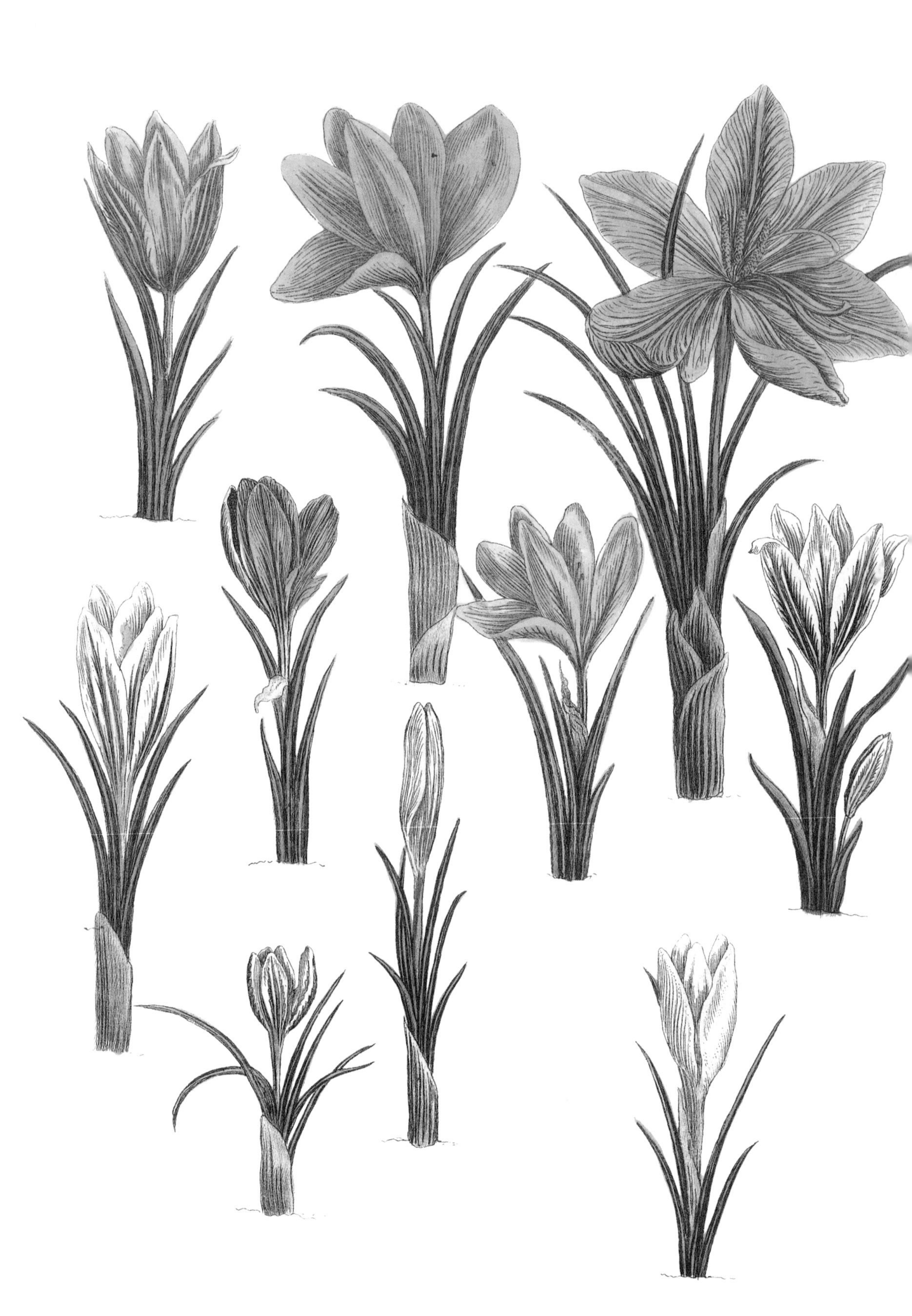

JANUARY

Monday 20

Holiday, USA (Martin Luther King's birthday)

Tuesday 21

RHS London Flower Show

Wednesday 22

RHS London Flower Show

Thursday 23

Friday 24

Last Quarter

Saturday 25

Sunday 26

The saffron crocus (*Crocus sativus*), engraved by Bartholomaeus Seuter, from the second volume of *Phytanthoza* (1739)

JANUARY ~ FEBRUARY

27 *Monday*

Holiday, Australia (Australia Day)

28 *Tuesday*

29 *Wednesday*

30 *Thursday*

31 *Friday*

1 *Saturday*

New Moon

Chinese New Year

2 *Sunday*

WEEK 5

A form of banana (*Musa*), engraved by Bartholomaeus Seuter or Johann Jakob Haid, from the first volume of *Phytanthoza* (1737)

FEBRUARY

Monday 3

Tuesday 4

Wednesday 5

Thursday 6

Holiday, New Zealand (Waitangi Day)

Friday 7

Saturday 8

First Quarter

Sunday 9

WEEK 6

The night-blooming cereus (*Selenicereus grandiflorus*), engraved by Johann Jakob Haid, from the second volume of *Phytanthoza* (1739)

FEBRUARY

10 Monday

---

11 Tuesday

---

12 Wednesday

Holiday, USA (Lincoln's Birthday)

---

13 Thursday

---

14 Friday

St Valentine's Day

---

15 Saturday

---

16 Sunday

Full Moon

WEEK 7

Varieties of primroses and cowslips (*Primula veris*), engraved by Bartholomaeus Seuter, from the fourth volume of *Phytanthoza* (1745)

FEBRUARY

Monday 17

Holiday, USA (Presidents' Day)

Tuesday 18

RHS London Flower Show

Wednesday 19

RHS London Flower Show

Thursday 20

Friday 21

Saturday 22

Last Quarter

Sunday 23

WEEK 8

Forms of chilli peppers (*Capsicum annuum*), engraved by Johann Jakob Haid, from the fourth volume of *Phytanthoza* (1745)

FEBRUARY ~ MARCH

24 Monday

25 Tuesday

26 Wednesday

27 Thursday

28 Friday

1 Saturday

St David's Day

2 Sunday

WEEK 9

Varieties of carrot (*Daucus carota*), engraved by Johann Jakob Haid, from the second volume of *Phytanthoza* (1739)

MARCH

Monday 3

New Moon

Tuesday 4

Shrove Tuesday
RHS London Flower Show

Wednesday 5

Ash Wednesday
Islamic New Year (subject to sighting of the moon)
RHS London Flower Show

Thursday 6

Friday 7

Saturday 8

Sunday 9

WEEK 10

Varieties of heartsease (*Viola tricolor*), engraved by Johann Jakob Haid, from the third volume of *Phytanthoza* (1742)

MARCH

10 Monday

Commonwealth Day

11 Tuesday

First Quarter

12 Wednesday

13 Thursday

RHS London Orchid Show

14 Friday

RHS London Orchid Show

15 Saturday

RHS London Orchid Show

16 Sunday

RHS London Orchid Show

WEEK 11

Daffodil cultivars, engraved by Bartholomaeus Seuter, from the third volume of *Phytanthoza* (1742)

MARCH

Monday 17

St Patrick's Day
Holiday, Northern Ireland and Republic of Ireland

Full Moon

Tuesday 18

Wednesday 19

Thursday 20

Friday 21

Vernal Equinox

Saturday 22

Sunday 23

WEEK 12

Cultivars of *Fritillaria meleagris*, engraved by Bartholomaeus Seuter or Johann Jakob Haid, from the second volume of *Phytanthoza* (1739)

MARCH

24 Monday

25 Tuesday

Last Quarter

26 Wednesday

27 Thursday

28 Friday

29 Saturday

30 Sunday

Mothering Sunday, UK
British Summer Time begins

Wallflowers (*Erysimum cheiri*, formerly *Cheiranthus cheiri*), engraved by Johann Jakob Haid, from the third volume of *Phytanthoza* (1742)

MARCH ~ APRIL

Monday 31

New Moon

Tuesday 1

Wednesday 2

Thursday 3

Friday 4

Saturday 5

Sunday 6

WEEK 14

Tulip cultivars, engraved by Johann Jakob Haid, from the fourth volume of *Phytanthoza* (1745)

APRIL

7 Monday

8 Tuesday

9 Wednesday *First Quarter*

10 Thursday

11 Friday

12 Saturday

13 Sunday

Palm Sunday

WEEK 15

Cultivars of crown imperial (*Fritillaria imperialis*),
engraved by Bartholomaeus Seuter, from the
third volume of *Phytanthoza* (1742)

APRIL

Monday 14

Tuesday 15

Full Moon

Wednesday 16

Thursday 17

Maundy Thursday
Passover (Pesach), First Day

Friday 18

Good Friday
Holiday, UK, Republic of Ireland, Canada, USA, Australia and New Zealand

Saturday 19

Sunday 20

Easter Sunday

WEEK 16

Two forms of the white or madonna lily (*Lilium candidum*), engraved by Bartholomaeus Seuter, from the third volume of *Phytanthoza* (1742)

APRIL

21 Monday

Easter Monday,
Holiday, UK (exc.Scotland), Republic of Ireland, Canada, Australia and New Zealand
Birthday of Queen Elizabeth II

22 Tuesday

23 Wednesday

Last Quarter

St George's Day
Passover (Pesach), Seventh Day

24 Thursday

Passover (Pesach), Eighth Day

25 Friday

Holiday, Australia and New Zealand (Anzac Day)

26 Saturday

27 Sunday

WEEK 17

Forms of *Iris germanica*, *Iris susiana* and *Iris xiphium*, engraved by Bartholomaeus Seuter, from the third volume of *Phytanthoza* (1742)

APRIL ~ MAY

Monday 28

Tuesday 29

RHS London Flower Show (to be confirmed)

Wednesday 30

RHS London Flower Show (to be confirmed)

New Moon

Thursday 1

Friday 2

Saturday 3

Sunday 4

WEEK 18

Forms of *Tradescantia virginiana*, engraved by Johann Jakob Haid, from the second volume of *Phytanthoza* (1739)

MAY

5 Monday

Early May Bank Holiday, UK and Republic of Ireland

6 Tuesday

7 Wednesday

8 Thursday

9 Friday

First Quarter

Malvern Spring Gardening Show

10 Saturday

Malvern Spring Gardening Show

11 Sunday

Mother's Day, Canada, USA, Australia and New Zealand
Malvern Spring Gardening Show

WEEK 19

Cultivars of foxglove (*Digitalis purpurea*), engraved by Bartholomaeus Seuter, from the second volume of *Phytanthoza* (1739)

MAY

Monday 12

Tuesday 13

Wednesday 14

Thursday 15

Full Moon

Friday 16

Saturday 17

Sunday 18

WEEK 20

Cultivars of peony (*Paeonia mascula*), engraved by Johann Jakob Haid, from the fourth volume of *Phytanthoza* (1745)

MAY

19 Monday

Holiday, Canada (Victoria Day)

20 Tuesday

Chelsea Flower Show

21 Wednesday

Chelsea Flower Show

22 Thursday

Chelsea Flower Show

23 Friday

Last Quarter

Chelsea Flower Show

24 Saturday

25 Sunday

WEEK 21

Four cultivars (now vanished) of the corn poppy (*Papaver rhoeas*), engraved by Bartholomaeus Seuter, from the fourth volume of *Phytanthoza* (1745)

MAY ~ JUNE

Monday 26

Spring Bank Holiday, UK
Holiday, USA (Memorial Day)

Tuesday 27

Wednesday 28

Thursday 29

Ascension Day

Friday 30

New Moon

Saturday 31

Sunday 1

WEEK 22

Flowers of tobacco (*Nicotiana*) and love-in-a-mist (*Nigella*), engraved by Johann Jakob Haid, from the third volume of *Phytanthoza* (1742)

JUNE

2 Monday

Holiday, Republic of Ireland
Holiday, New Zealand (The Queen's birthday)

3 Tuesday

4 Wednesday

5 Thursday

6 Friday

Jewish Feast of Weeks (Shavuot)

7 Saturday

First Quarter

8 Sunday

Whit Sunday (Pentecost)

WEEK 23

Ornamental alliums (*Allium moly*), engraved by Bartholomaeus Seuter, from the third volume of *Phytanthoza* (1742)

JUNE

Monday 9

Holiday, Australia (The Queen's birthday)

Tuesday 10

Wednesday 11

BBC Gardeners' World Live, Birmingham

Thursday 12

BBC Gardeners' World Live, Birmingham

Friday 13

BBC Gardeners' World Live, Birmingham

Full Moon

Saturday 14

The Queen's official birthday (subject to confirmation)
BBC Gardeners' World Live, Birmingham

Sunday 15

Trinity Sunday
Father's Day, UK, Canada and USA
BBC Gardeners' World Live, Birmingham

Forms of *Rosa gallica*, engraved by Johann Jakob Haid, from the fourth volume of *Phytanthoza* (1745)

JUNE

16 Monday

17 Tuesday

18 Wednesday

19 Thursday

Corpus Christi

20 Friday

21 Saturday

Last Quarter

Summer Solstice

22 Sunday

WEEK 25

An early parrot tulip, engraved by Johann Jakob Haid, from the fourth volume of *Phytanthoza* (1745)

JUNE

Monday 23

Tuesday 24

First Wisley Flower Show (to be confirmed)

Wednesday 25

First Wisley Flower Show (to be confirmed)

Thursday 26

First Wisley Flower Show (to be confirmed)

Friday 27

Saturday 28

New Moon

Sunday 29

Cultivars (now vanished) of the corn poppy (*Papaver rhoeas*), engraved by Bartholomaeus Seuter, from the fourth volume of *Phytanthoza* (1745)

JUNE ~ JULY

30 Monday

1 Tuesday

Holiday, Canada (Canada Day)

2 Wednesday

3 Thursday

4 Friday

Holiday, USA (Independence Day)

5 Saturday

6 Sunday

WEEK 27

Four single-flowered *Campanula* cultivars, engraved by Johann Jakob Haid, from the second volume of *Phytanthoza* (1739)

JULY

First Quarter *Monday 7*

Tuesday 8

Hampton Court Palace Flower Show

Wednesday 9

Hampton Court Palace Flower Show

Thursday 10

Hampton Court Palace Flower Show

Friday 11

Hampton Court Palace Flower Show

Saturday 12

Hampton Court Palace Flower Show

Full Moon *Sunday 13*

Hampton Court Palace Flower Show

Apricot varieties, engraved by Johann Jakob Haid, from the third volume of *Phytanthoza* (1742)

JULY

14 Monday

Holiday, Northern Ireland (Battle of the Boyne)

15 Tuesday

St Swithin's Day

16 Wednesday

17 Thursday

18 Friday

19 Saturday

20 Sunday

WEEK 29

Cultivars of carnation (*Dianthus caryophyllus*), engraved by Johann Jakob Haid, from the second volume of *Phytanthoza* (1739)

JULY

Last Quarter — *Monday 21*

Tuesday 22

Wednesday 23

The RHS Flower Show at Tatton Park

Thursday 24

The RHS Flower Show at Tatton Park

Friday 25

The RHS Flower Show at Tatton Park

Saturday 26

The RHS Flower Show at Tatton Park

Sunday 27

The RHS Flower Show at Tatton Park

WEEK 30

Varieties of larkspur (formerly *Delphinium ajacis* and now once again *Consolida ajacis*), engraved by Bartholomaeus Seuter, from the second volume of *Phytanthoza* (1739)

JULY ~ AUGUST

28 Monday

29 Tuesday *New Moon*

30 Wednesday

31 Thursday

1 Friday

2 Saturday

3 Sunday

WEEK 31

Cultivars of hollyhocks (*Alcea rosea*), engraved by Johann Jakob Haid, from the third volume of *Phytanthoza* (1742)

AUGUST

Monday 4

Summer Bank Holiday, Scotland and Republic of Ireland

First Quarter

Tuesday 5

Wednesday 6

Thursday 7

Friday 8

Saturday 9

Sunday 10

Echinops sphaerocephalus, engraved by Bartholomaeus Seuter, from the second volume of *Phytanthoza* (1739)

AUGUST

11 Monday

12 Tuesday — *Full Moon*

13 Wednesday

14 Thursday

15 Friday

16 Saturday

17 Sunday

Forms of waterlily (*Nymphaea alba*), engraved by Johann Jakob Haid, from the third volume of *Phytanthoza* (1742)

AUGUST

Monday 18

Tuesday 19

Second Wisley Flower Show (to be confirmed)

Wednesday 20

Last Quarter

Second Wisley Flower Show (to be confirmed)

Thursday 21

Second Wisley Flower Show (to be confirmed)

Friday 22

Saturday 23

Sunday 24

WEEK 34

The canna (*Canna indica*), engraved by Johann Jakob Haid, from the second volume of *Phytanthoza* (1739)

AUGUST

25 Monday

Summer Bank Holiday, UK (exc. Scotland)

26 Tuesday

27 Wednesday

New Moon

28 Thursday

29 Friday

30 Saturday

31 Sunday

WEEK 35

The sunflower (*Helianthus annuus*), engraved by Johann Jakob Haid, from the second volume of *Phytanthoza* (1739)

SEPTEMBER

Monday 1

Holiday, Canada (Labour Day) and USA (Labor Day)

Tuesday 2

First Quarter

Wednesday 3

Thursday 4

Friday 5

Saturday 6

Sunday 7

Father's Day, Australia and New Zealand

WEEK 36

A variety of maize (*Zea mays*), engraved by Johann Jakob Haid, from the second volume of *Phytanthoza* (1739)

SEPTEMBER

8 Monday

9 Tuesday

10 Wednesday *Full Moon*

11 Thursday

12 Friday

13 Saturday

14 Sunday

WEEK 37

Varieties of wheat (*Triticum*), engraved by Johann Jakob Haid, from the fourth volume of *Phytanthoza* (1745)

SEPTEMBER

Monday 15

Tuesday 16

RHS Great Autumn Show, London

Wednesday 17

RHS Great Autumn Show, London

Last Quarter

Thursday 18

Friday 19

Saturday 20

Sunday 21

WEEK 38

A grape variety used for making white wine, engraved by Bartholomaeus Seuter, from the fourth volume of *Phytanthoza* (1745)

SEPTEMBER

22 *Monday*

23 *Tuesday*

Autumnal Equinox

24 *Wednesday*

25 *Thursday*

26 *Friday*

New Moon

27 *Saturday*

Jewish New Year (Rosh Hashanah)
Malvern Autumn Garden and Country Show

28 *Sunday*

Malvern Autumn Garden and Country Show

WEEK 39

Garden nasturtiums (*Tropaeolum minus*), engraved by Johann Jakob Haid, from the third volume of *Phytanthoza* (1742)

SEPTEMBER ~ OCTOBER

Monday 29

Michaelmas Day

Tuesday 30

Wednesday 1

First Quarter

Thursday 2

Friday 3

Saturday 4

Sunday 5

WEEK 40

Endive (*Cichorium endiva*), and *Tradescantia virginiana*, engraved by Johann Jakob Haid, from the second volume of *Phytanthoza* (1739)

OCTOBER

6 Monday

Jewish Day of Atonement (Yom Kippur)

7 Tuesday

RHS London Flower Show

8 Wednesday

RHS London Flower Show

9 Thursday

10 Friday

Full Moon

11 Saturday

Jewish Festival of Tabernacles (Succoth), First Day

12 Sunday

Apple varieties, engraved by Bartholomaeus Seuter, from the third volume of *Phytanthoza* (1742)

OCTOBER

Monday 13

Holiday, Canada (Thanksgiving Day)
Holiday, USA (Columbus Day)

Tuesday 14

Wednesday 15

Thursday 16

Friday 17

Last Quarter

Saturday 18

Jewish Festival of Tabernacles (Succoth), Eighth Day

Sunday 19

WEEK 42

A variety of cyclamen (*Cyclamen hederifolium*), engraved by Bartholomaeus Seuter, from the second volume of *Phytanthoza* (1739)

OCTOBER

20 Monday

21 Tuesday

22 Wednesday

23 Thursday

24 Friday

United Nations Day

25 Saturday

New Moon

26 Sunday

British Summer Time ends

WEEK 43

Plum varieties, engraved by Bartholomaeus Seuter, from the fourth volume of *Phytanthoza* (1745)

OCTOBER ~ NOVEMBER

Monday 27

First Day of Ramadân (subject to sighting of the moon)
Holiday, Republic of Ireland
Holiday, New Zealand (Labour Day)

Tuesday 28

Wednesday 29

Thursday 30

Friday 31

Hallowe'en

First Quarter

Saturday 1

All Saints' Day

Sunday 2

WEEK 44

Two forms of oleander (*Nerium oleander*), engraved by Johann Jakob Haid, from the third volume of *Phytanthoza* (1742)

NOVEMBER

3 Monday

4 Tuesday

5 Wednesday

Guy Fawkes' Day

6 Thursday

7 Friday

8 Saturday

9 Sunday

Full Moon

Remembrance Sunday, UK

WEEK 45

The jambolan or Java plum (*Syzygium cumini*), engraved by Bartholomaeus Seuter, from the third volume of *Phytanthoza* (1742)

NOVEMBER

Monday 10

Tuesday 11

Holiday, Canada (Remembrance Day)
Holiday, USA (Veterans' Day)

Wednesday 12

Thursday 13

Friday 14

Saturday 15

Sunday 16

WEEK 46

Two species of thorn-apple (*Datura stramonium* and *D. meteloides*), engraved by Bartholomaeus Seuter, from the fourth volume of *Phytanthoza* (1745)

NOVEMBER

17 Monday *Last Quarter*

18 Tuesday

19 Wednesday

20 Thursday

21 Friday

22 Saturday

23 Sunday *New Moon*

WEEK 47

Chanterelles and other fungi, engraved by Johann Jakob Haid, from the second volume of *Phytanthoza* (1739)

NOVEMBER

Monday 24

Tuesday 25

RHS London Flower Show

Wednesday 26

RHS London Flower Show

Thursday 27

Holiday, USA (Thanksgiving Day)

Friday 28

Saturday 29

First Quarter

Sunday 30

St Andrew's Day
Advent Sunday

WEEK 48

A melon (*Cucumis melo*), engraved by Bartholomaeus Seuter, from the third volume of *Phytanthoza* (1742)

DECEMBER

1 *Monday*

2 *Tuesday*

3 *Wednesday*

4 *Thursday*

5 *Friday*

6 *Saturday*

7 *Sunday*

WEEK 49

Pear varieties, engraved by Bartholomaeus Seuter,
from the fourth volume of *Phytanthoza* (1745)

DECEMBER

Full Moon — *Monday 8*

Tuesday 9

Wednesday 10

Thursday 11

Friday 12

Saturday 13

Sunday 14

WEEK 50

Cultivars of the garden ranunculus (*Ranunculus asiaticus*), engraved by Bartholomaeus Seuter, from the fourth volume of *Phytanthoza* (1745)

DECEMBER

15 Monday

16 Tuesday

Last Quarter

17 Wednesday

18 Thursday

19 Friday

20 Saturday

Jewish Festival of Chanukah, First Day

21 Sunday

WEEK 51

Protea scolymocephala, engraved by Bartholomaeus Seuter, from the fourth volume of *Phytanthoza* (1745)

DECEMBER

Monday 22

Winter Solstice

Tuesday 23

New Moon

Wednesday 24

Christmas Eve

Thursday 25

Christmas Day
Holiday UK, Republic of Ireland, Canada, USA, Australia and New Zealand

Friday 26

Boxing Day (St Stephen's Day)
Holiday UK, Republic of Ireland, Canada, Australia and New Zealand

Saturday 27

Jewish Festival of Chanukah, Eighth Day

Sunday 28

WEEK 52

Three species of *Pinus* – the Scots pine (*P. sylvestris*), the stone pine (*P. pinea*) and the Weymouth pine (*P. strobus*) – engraved by Johann Jakob Haid, from the fourth volume of Phytanthoza (1745)

DECEMBER ~ JANUARY

29 Monday

30 Tuesday

First Quarter

31 Wednesday

New Year's Eve

1 Thursday

New Year's Day
Holiday, UK, Republic of Ireland, Canada, USA, Australia and New Zealand

2 Friday

Holiday, Scotland and New Zealand

3 Saturday

4 Sunday

WEEK 1, 2004

The horse chestnut (*Aesculus hippocastanum*), engraved by Johann Jakob Haid, from the second volume of *Phytanthoza* (1739)

European National Holidays 2003

Holidays that fall on a Sunday are not included

AUSTRIA	Jan. 1, 6; April 21; May 1, 29; June 9, 19; Aug. 15; Nov. 1; Dec. 8, 25, 26
BELGIUM	Jan. 1; April 21; May 1, 29; June 9; July 21; Aug. 15; Nov. 1, 11; Dec. 25
DENMARK	Jan. 1; April 17, 18, 21; May 16, 29; June 5, 9; Dec. 25, 26
FINLAND	Jan. 1, 6; April 18, 21; May 1, 29; June 21; Nov. 1; Dec. 6, 25, 26
FRANCE	Jan. 1; April 21; May 1, 8, 29; June 9; July 14; August 15; Nov. 1, 11; Dec. 25
GERMANY	Jan. 1, 6; April 18, 21; May 1, 29; June 9, 19; Aug. 15; Oct. 3, 31; Nov. 1, 19; Dec. 25, 26
GREECE	Jan. 1, 6; Mar. 10, 25; April 25, 28; May 1; June 16; Aug. 15; Oct. 28; Dec. 25, 26
ITALY	Jan. 1, 6; April 21, 25; May 1; Aug. 15; Nov. 1; Dec. 8, 25, 26
LUXEMBOURG	Jan. 1; Mar. 3; April 21; May 1, 29; June 9, 23; Aug. 15; Nov. 1; Dec. 25, 26
NETHERLANDS	Jan. 1; April 18, 21, 30; May 5, 29; June 9; Dec. 25, 26
NORWAY	Jan. 1; April 17, 18, 21; May 1, 17, 29; June 9; Dec. 25, 26
PORTUGAL	Jan. 1; Mar. 4; April 18, 25; May 1; June 10, 19; Aug. 15; Nov. 1; Dec. 1, 8, 25
SPAIN	Jan. 1, 6; Mar. 19; April 17, 18, 21; May 1; July 25; Aug. 15; Nov. 1; Dec. 6, 8, 25, 26
SWEDEN	Jan. 1, 6; April 18, 21; May 1, 29; June 9, 21; Nov. 1; Dec. 25, 26
SWITZERLAND	Jan. 1; April 18, 21; May 1, 29; June 9; Aug. 1; Nov. 1; Dec. 25, 26